Asteroids

Brandon Robshaw and Rochelle Scholar

Published in association with The Basic Skills Agency

Hodder & Stoughton

A MEMBER OF THE HODDER HEADLINE GROUP

Acknowledgements
Cover artwork: David A. Hardy © Science Photo Library

Illustrations: Brian Lee

Photos: pp. 5, 14, 18, 22, 26 © Corbis; p. 8 © Joe Tucciarone/Science Photo Library.

Orders: please contact Bookpoint Ltd, 130 Milton Park, Abingdon, Oxon OX14 4SB. Telephone: (44) 01235 827720, Fax: (44) 01235 400454. Lines are open from 9.00 – 6.00, Monday to Saturday, with a 24 hour message answering service. Email address: orders@bookpoint.co.uk

British Library Cataloguing in Publication Data
A catalogue record for this title is available from The British Library

ISBN 0 340 84865 0

First published 2002
Impression number 10 9 8 7 6 5 4 3 2 1
Year 2007 2006 2005 2004 2003 2002

Typeset by SX Composing DTP, Rayleigh, Essex.
Printed in Great Britain for Hodder & Stoughton Educational, a division of Hodder Headline Plc, 338 Euston Road, London NW1 3BH by The Bath Press Ltd.

Contents

1 The Death of the Dinosaurs

The Earth, 65 million years ago.
At that time, there were no humans.
There were very few mammals.
The Earth was ruled by dinosaurs.
Giant creatures that roamed
through the swamps and forests.
They were far bigger than any
land animals alive today.

Then something happened.
An object from space
came speeding towards the Earth.
It was an asteroid.
It was about 10 km across.
It was moving at 50 km per second.
It smashed into the Earth . . .

BANG!

The impact was like
all the nuclear bombs in the world
going off at once.
The whole of the Earth heated up.
Dinosaurs out in the open were burned alive.
Trees and plants caught fire.
Fires burned all over the planet.

Then, very slowly,
the Earth cooled down again.
A thick layer of smoke and dust
rose into the sky and hid the sun.
For months, it was dark and very cold.
Any dinosaurs still alive died of cold.

At last the sky cleared –
but the danger wasn't over.
Acid rain and choking dust
fell to Earth.

In the end, seventy per cent
of all animals on Earth were wiped out.

The dinosaurs were gone.
In future, Earth would be ruled by mammals.

2 What is an Asteroid?

Scientists think it very likely
that this is how the dinosaurs died out.
A comet or asteroid did fall to Earth
65 million years ago.
Scientists call it 'The Doomsday Comet'.

It left a crater in Mexico.
The crater is 180 km wide.
It would have caused great heat
and tidal waves.
Then months of cold.
Then falls of acid rain and choking dust.
So it is very likely
that this killed the dinosaurs.

So, what is an asteroid?
And what is a comet?

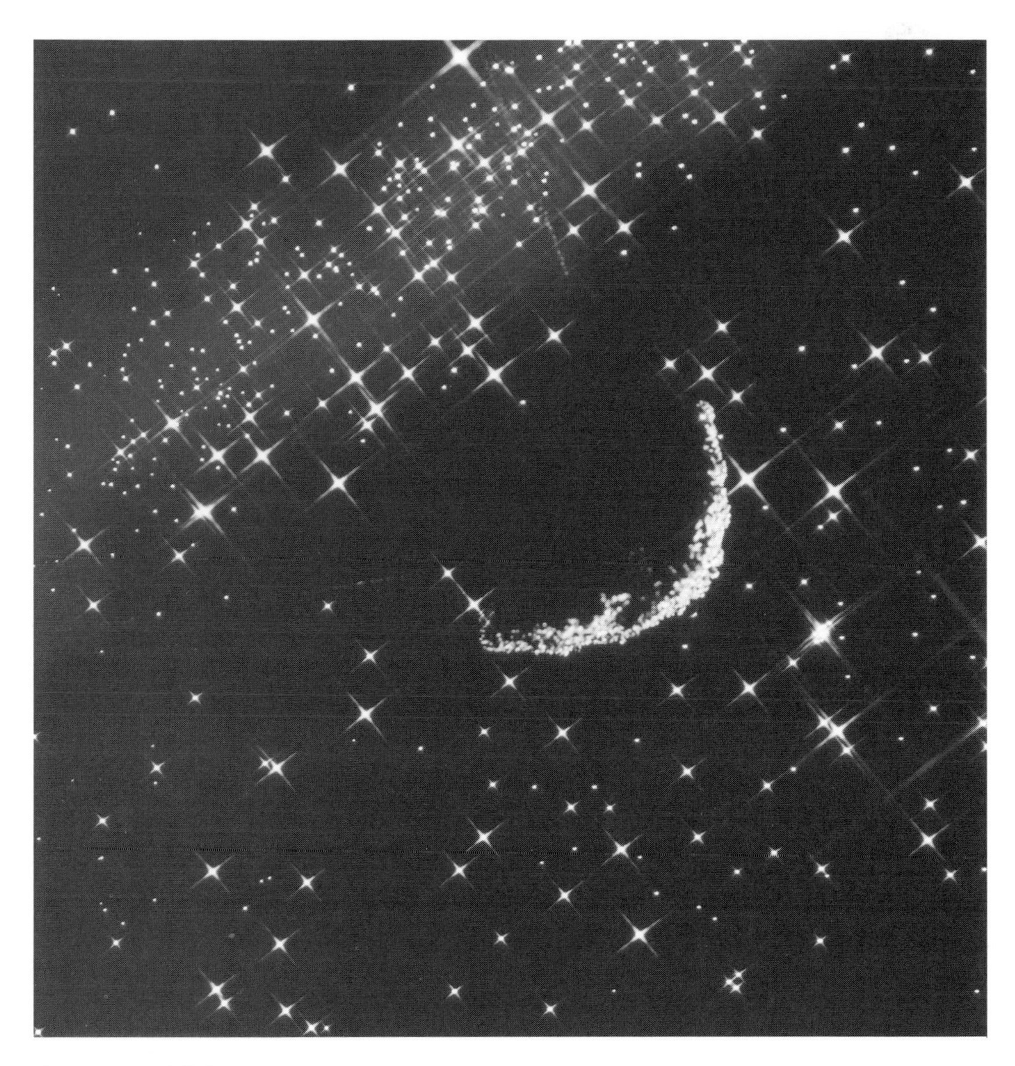

An asteroid in space.

Asteroids first.
An asteroid is a big chunk of rock in space.
The biggest known asteroid is 933 km across.
The smallest are less than 1 km across.

Asteroids do not keep still.
They travel round the sun,
just as the planets do.

Even the biggest asteroids
are too small to see with the naked eye.
You need a telescope.
All you would see
is a tiny point of light.
This is caused by the sun shining on it.

Anyone who discovers an asteroid in space
can choose a name for it.
Other objects in space,
such as planets or comets,
are named after the person who found them.
But if you find an asteroid,
you can call it anything.
You could name it after your cat if you wanted.

3 The Asteroid Belt

Most asteroids are found
in the asteroid belt.
This is a large group of asteroids
between Mars and Jupiter.
They are hundreds of millions
of kilometres away from Earth.

The first asteroid was discovered in 1801.
It is called Ceres.
It is the largest of the asteroids,
at 933 km across.

Since then about 8000 large asteroids
have been found.
But there must be millions of smaller ones.
Scientists think there are about
nine million asteroids
of four kilometres across or less.

Asteroids approaching Earth.

Unlike planets, most asteroids are not round.
They are rough lumps of rock,
all different shapes and sizes.

We have close-range photos of some of them.
The space-probe Galileo took pictures
on its way to Jupiter.
They are covered in craters
where meteors have hit them
One of them has a tiny moon going round it.

Most asteroids in the asteroid belt
are no danger to Earth.
They travel round the sun –
this journey is called an orbit.
Most asteroids stay in their orbit.

Sometimes, however,
they are disturbed.
This may be from
bumping into another asteroid.
It flies out of the asteroid belt
and across space.
Such an asteroid is called a rogue asteroid.
There is a danger that
a rogue asteroid may hit the Earth.

4 Comets

What is a comet?
Like asteroids,
comets travel in an orbit round the sun.

A comet has three parts.
The solid part is called the nucleus.
It is a mass of ice and rocks.
The nucleus is usually about 10 km across,
but it can be up to 100 km across.

Around the nucleus is a cloud of gas.
This is called the coma.
It may be as much as 1 million km across.

The third part is the comet's tail.
The tail is a long stream of dust.
It could be ten million kilometres long.

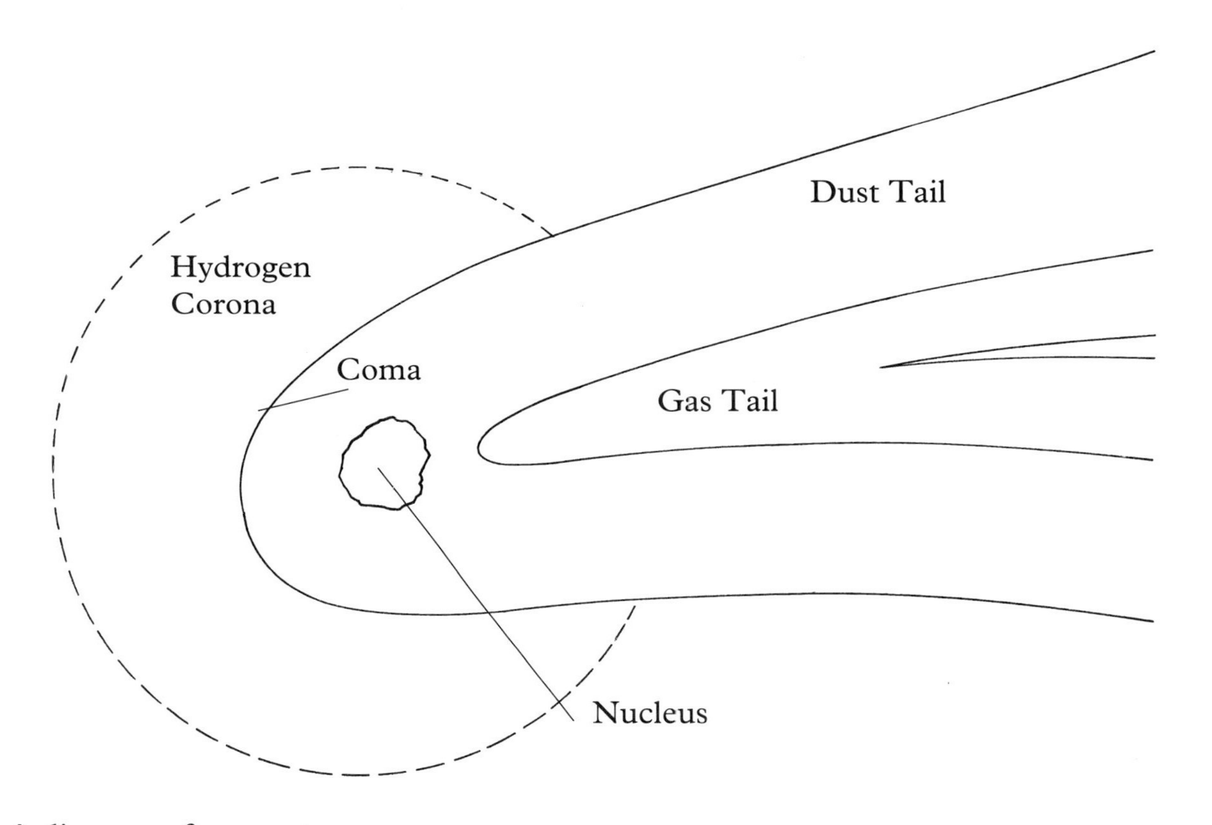

A diagram of a comet.

Most comets are further out in space
than asteroids.
They have much longer orbits.
This means that it takes them much longer
to go round the sun.
The nearest take about twenty years
to orbit the sun.
The furthest could take one million years
to go round the sun just once.

Some comets pass quite close to Earth.
Some can be seen in the night sky
with the naked eye.
Like Halley's comet.
This was discovered by the scientist,
Edmund Halley, in 1695.
It takes 76 years to orbit the sun.
It was last seen in 1999 –
so if you missed it,
you've got a long time to wait!

Could a comet hit Earth?
It's possible.
A comet hit Jupiter in 1994.

5 Meteors

Asteroids and comets are not the only objects
flying around in space.
There are also meteors.

Meteors are much smaller than
asteroids or comets.
A meteor is a small chunk of rock.
Meteors are made when asteroids hit each other
and bits fly off.

A meteor may be as tiny as a grain of sand
or it may be several metres wide.
If it's much larger,
then it is called an asteroid.
Meteors are really very small rogue asteroids.

A shooting star.

Meteors often fall towards the Earth.
They travel so fast that
when they hit the earth's atmosphere,
they burn up.
This makes them shine brightly in the night sky –
and that's what a shooting star is.
A meteor burning away.
There are two nights in the year
when it's easy to see shooting stars.
You can see whole showers of them
on 12 August and 13 December.
The earth passes through
meteor streams at those times.

Most meteors don't reach
the Earth's surface.
They burn away
before they get there.
But some of the bigger ones
do reach the Earth.
They are then called meteorites.
Meteorites are usually pretty small,
like pebbles.
But some are bigger.

A very large meteorite –
about 70 metres across –
fell to Earth about 25,000 years ago.
The crater it left is still there
in Arizona, USA.
The crater is 12 km wide
and 180 metres deep.

You can imagine the damage
that would be done
if a meteorite that size hit Earth today.

6 Craters

Our solar system is very, very big.
Most of it is empty space.
The asteroid belt is about 500 million km away.
You may think that the chances
of Earth being hit by an asteroid
are very, very small.

You'd be right.
The chances are very small indeed.
So small, it only happens every few million years.
But every few million years, it does happen.

The surface of the moon is full of craters.
These were left by asteroids, comets and meteors.
Over millions and millions of years,
the moon has been hit again and again.

A crater on Earth.

There are craters on the Earth, too.
They are not so easy to spot as on the moon.
On Earth, craters get worn away by wind and rain.
Or covered by trees,
or filled with water.
But they are there –
and they show that the Earth
does get hit from time to time.

Scientists have studied the Earth's craters.
They have measured them.
They have worked out how old they are.
And they have worked out how often they happen.

A crater around 20 km wide
is made about every 380,000 years.
A crater around 26 km wide
is made about every 640,000 years.

A 26 km crater would be made by an asteroid
about 1 km across.
This would do a lot of damage
and cause a lot of deaths.
But it would not destroy
the whole of civilisation.

To do that, a bigger asteroid would be needed.
An asteroid that is 4 km across would do it.

Scientists have worked out that this happens
about every ten million years.

Ten million years is a very long time.
Too long for us to worry about?
Maybe not.
We know it will happen at some time
in the next ten million years.
But we don't know when, exactly.
It could be next year.
Probably not.
But it could be.

We don't expect it next year.
But the dinosaurs didn't expect
the one that hit the Earth 65 million years ago.

7 If it Happened Tomorrow . . .

Why would an asteroid hitting the Earth
be such a disaster?

An asteroid that is 4 km across
may sound pretty big.
It would look pretty big
if you saw it falling down on your head.

Still, compared to the size of the Earth it's tiny.
The Earth is 12,756 km across.
How could an asteroid so much smaller
do so much damage?

The main reason is its speed.
An asteroid can travel at up to
50 km per second.
So, if you were standing next to it,
a second later it would be 50 km away.

The Earth from space.

The Earth is moving too.
It travels at 2000 km an hour.
So when the two bodies hit,
the impact comes from their
two speeds put together.

When something that fast
stops so suddenly,
it releases a massive amount of energy.
This is where all the heat comes from.
An asteroid that is 4 km across
would cause a massive explosion
when hitting the earth.
It would be like 4 million atom bombs
all going off at once.

If the asteroid was bigger,
the explosion would be bigger.
The one that hit the Earth 65 million years ago
was about ten kilometres across.
If this hit us tomorrow,
it would destroy all human life.

First the shock and heat
would kill anyone living within
a few hundred kilometres.
Then the heat would spread all over the planet
in a few hours.
At the same time,
there would be lots of other, smaller explosions.
Bits of the asteroids that flew off at impact
would fall back on to the Earth as missiles.

Most people would be burned to death.
There would also be huge tidal waves
caused by the shock.
These would destroy whole cities.

Then, as the planet cooled down,
thick clouds of dust and smoke
would fill the air.
The sun would be hidden for months.
It would be dark and very cold.
It would be impossible to grow food.
Anyone left alive would die
of cold or hunger.

8 What can we do?

It is not very likely
that an asteroid will hit the Earth
in the near future.
Still, it is possible.
Is there anything we can do
to make sure it does not happen?

The main thing is to plot the orbits of all
the large rogue asteroids in our solar system.
Then we will know
if an asteroid is coming our way.

This is a very big job.
Scientists already know the orbits
of about a hundred asteroids that cross
the Earth's orbit.
But there could be as many as 1800 rogue asteroids
that cross our orbit.

A scientist operating radio telecopes.

Then there are all the asteroids in the asteroid belt.
We are safe from these –
but it would help to know their orbits.
Then, if their orbit changes
we will have warning.

Once we know the orbits of all the asteroids,
we need to blow up any
which might hit the Earth.

This is something we cannot yet do.
We don't have the technology to blow up
an object moving at high speed far out in space.

In the future,
we could have the technology to do this.
Until then, we'd better keep our fingers crossed.

Glossary

Asteroid	A large chunk of rock in space. Some are big enough to be small planets. They travel round the Sun.
Comet	An object in space made up of a core of rock, dust and ice and a long tail of dust. Comets travel round the Sun.
Crater	The hollow left in the ground when an asteroid or comet hits a planet.
Meteor	A small chunk of rock in space. Meteors are smaller than 1 km across.
Meteorite	A meteor that falls to Earth.
Orbit	The path around the Sun of a planet, comet or asteroid. Most orbits are oval.
Rogue asteroid	An asteroid that has left its orbit and is wandering through space.
Space-probe	An unmanned spaceship, sent to explore space and send back information.